Tai Chi

This book is dedicated to the love of my life, my wife Alexandra

Thorsons First Directions

Tai Chi

Paul Brecher

Thorsons
An Imprint of HarperCollins*Publishers*
77–85 Fulham Palace Road,
Hammersmith, London W6 8JB

Published by Thorsons 2000
10 9 8 7 6 5 4 3 2 1

Text copyright © Paul Brecher 2000
Copyright © Thorsons 2000

Editor: Caroline Wheal
Design: Wheelhouse Creative
Photography: Henry Allen and PhotoDisc Europe Ltd.

Text derived from *Principles of Tai Chi*
published by Thorsons 1997

Paul Brecher asserts the moral right to
be identified as the author of this work

A catalogue record for this book
is available from the British Library

ISBN 0 0071 0339 5

Printed and bound in Hong Kong

Contents

Tai Chi

is a martial art from ancient China, for healing and

elf development as well as self defence

Forward

I met Paul Brecher some years back when he visited me here in Australia as part of a 'searching out' worldwide tour.

He was then, and is now, a genuine young man with a passion for his Taijiquan (Tai Chi Chuan). I showed Paul the Old Yang Style of Taijiquan and from then on he was hooked on this explosive form which is unlike any other Taijiquan.

Over the years, Paul studied hard and attended every workshop that I gave in London. He also visited me here in Australia from time to time to train.

Now, he has written an excellent book on Taijiquan. You will discover in this book things that have not been written about Taijiquan before, simply because the other authors have not known about the older style of Taijiquan. For many years my voice rang out clear but not many noticed. Nowadays the Old Yang Style of Taijiquan is well recognized but not many outside the World Taiji Boxing Association know how to perform or teach this style.

Paul has presented a well thought out work on the principles of Taijiquan for both beginners and advanced students of the art, no matter what style they practise.

Having read this book, the reader will probably wish to get in touch with a teacher of this style of Taijiquan. Nowadays, luckily, we have many such teachers all around the world, including Paul Brecher in London.

This book will add a new dimension to your Taijiquan and internal martial arts training and will grace a good place on your bookshelf.

Erle Montaigue
Master Degree China
World Chief of the World Taiji Boxing Association

What is Tai Chi?

Tai Chi is a martial art that originated in China over one thousand years ago. It was originally used for self-defence but today most people practise it for the great health benefits it has to offer, and for self and spiritual development.

This book covers these aspects equally because they all enhance and balance each other out. For example, for a weak person to have good self defence skills, he needs to be healthier and stronger. A person who wants better health needs to develop a more positive attitude because the mind influences the body. And for the person who is trying to become more spiritual, practising Tai Chi for self defence helps to keep them grounded in the real world so that they don't get lost in the clouds.

The central part of any Tai Chi system is the form. This is a single person, empty-handed series of continuous, smooth, circular, flowing movements. Some forms contain a few movements and can be done in a few minutes, others contain many movements and can take over half an hour to complete.

Tai Chi also has many two-person sparring systems, such as Pushing Hands, Da Lu and San Sau, and weapons forms, such as the Sword and Dagger. Some styles of Tai Chi also contain explosive movements called Fa Jing. Fa means to release and Jing is internal force; so Fa Jing are sudden explosive releases of internal force.

Tai Chi is sometimes referred to as a soft style. Soft means that during training there is no unnecessary

Explosive Fa Jing movement ▶

tension in the muscles or mind. This allows for greater ease of movement and an increase in the circulation of blood and energy around the body, which in turn produces a state of relaxation and calm. These aspects of Tai Chi have made it attractive to many people as a type of stress release exercise.

Some people mistakenly think that soft means the movements are feeble and the attitude passive. On the contrary, the movements are dynamic and resilient, and the attitude is one of confidence and decisiveness. This positive attitude builds self confidence and has been shown to boost the immune system. Building a strong fighting spirit into Tai Chi also boosts the immune system.

Tai Chi is sometimes called an internal style: it is not just a form of physical exercise but also a type of Chi Kung. Chi Kung is a system of 'exercises that generate and circulate Chi energy around the body by following certain principles of posture, movement and breathing'.

For your Tai Chi to be a true internal style you need to incorporate into your training the Ten Points of Correct Tai Chi Posture, the Ten Internal Principles of Tai Chi and the Ten Methods of Practice of Tai Chi, all of which are explained in detail later on in this book. You will also find a section explaining Chi Kung.

What does Tai Chi mean?

Tai Chi is an abbreviation of Tai Chi Chuan. There is no single translation for these Chinese words; they carry many philosophical and poetical meanings as well as literal ones.

Tai Chi is the name of the Yin Yang symbol below. Chuan means fist, but implies martial art. So together Tai Chi Chuan means the 'Yin Yang fighting system'.

Tai Chi contains closed-fist punches, kicks and open-hand techniques like palm strikes and fingertip 'point strikes'. An experienced martial artist can recognize these moves in their Tai Chi forms, but many people, upon seeing the relaxed, smooth and flowing movements of Tai Chi for the first time, cannot believe that they have anything to do with a martial art.

The main aim of the Yin Yang theory is to attain a dynamic balance in all things at all levels. Tai Chi balances your energy, which connects with both the mind and the body, harmonizing them both.

Tai Chi should not be confused with Chi, which by itself means 'life force energy'; and Jing, which means 'internal force', should not be confused with Ching, which means 'vital essence' (hormones).

In this book, I have shortened Tai Chi Chuan to the more familiar term Tai Chi.

With this heel kick the power is ▶
created from turning the hip in the
opposite direction

How Did It All Start?

The majority of researchers agree that Tai Chi was created by Chang San Feng. He was born in 1270AD and spent his whole life studying Chinese martial arts and healing arts. He was a skilled acupuncturist and incorporated this knowledge into the Tai Chi style he created. After a successful career in government he retired to the Wudang mountain range to further develop his martial skill and spiritual nature. Eventually he organized his system into 12 forms called the Chi Disruption forms; they contain equal amounts of explosive Fa Jing movements and slow Chi Kung movements.

He reached an incredibly high level of ability and lived to be over a hundred years old. Legends say that he did not die, but transformed himself into pure spirit and flew away.

Chang wrote down some of his methods, which have been handed down from generation to generation and today form part of The Classics of Tai Chi. Here is my translation of an extract from his works:

The body must move as a single unit at one with the breath, Chi and Spirit.

The rooting of the feet, the strength of the legs and the power of the waist all manifest in the hands.

There is Connection within the whole body. Our movement is guided by our Intention.

Tai Chi is both rapid and calm
like the great river.

Chang San Feng (above) ▲

Yang Lu Chan 1799–1872 used the 12 Tai Chi ▶
Disruption forms to create his own system, known as the Old Yang Style of Tai Chi. A book of the main form in this style can be downloaded from www.taijiworld.com for free

What Can
It Do For Me?

When they practise Tai Chi, people with poor health become
stronger, and those with a tendency to be hyperactive become
more at ease. People who feel anxious become more confident,
and those who have an angry temperament feel calmer.
Eventually Tai Chi produces a happy, healing feeling in everyone.
For this reason Tai Chi Chuan is also translated as 'The Way of
Supreme Harmony'. You do not have to be Buddhist, Taoist, or of
any particular religion or race to gain from the practice of Tai Chi.

How does Tai Chi work?

Tai Chi heals the body by encouraging Chi (life force) to flow through the acupuncture meridians. Chi connects the mind and body with each other and the world. It is what the strands of 'the web of life' are made of.

The acupuncture meridians run through the entire body, connecting every part. They are different from the nerves, blood and lymphatic vessels, but they influence these and other body systems because they run through them all.

With age, the flow of Chi through the channels can be impaired by mental and physical tensions, poor diet, unhealthy lifestyle and illness.

When Tai Chi is practised daily, the flow of Chi through all the acupuncture meridians can be increased, and health and vitality regained. Many people come to Tai Chi later in life because of this wonderful rejuvenating aspect.

Each Tai Chi move slightly flexes a tendon, which encourages Chi to flow along the associated acupuncture meridian. The organs through which that meridian passes are energized and strengthened.

Muscles are relaxed during Tai Chi, so the flow of blood and Chi is not restricted. Where Chi goes, blood follows, so by increasing the Chi flow you boost the circulation of blood.

Each move generates centrifugal and centripetal forces which encourage the energy and blood to flow from the centre of the torso, out to the extremities, and back again, improving circulation without straining the heart. At the higher levels of Tai Chi, special abdominal breathing exercises are introduced which not only help generate and pump Chi around the body but also massage and strengthen the internal organs.

Animal qualities

Certain animals have qualities that Tai Chi practitioners want to develop: your health and self defence would benefit if you had the strong bones of a tiger, the vision of a bird of prey and the lightning speed of a striking snake. All Tai Chi movements are similar to those of a snake; the whole body rotates and twists continuously.

If you stand on one leg in a Tai Chi posture, you should have the strength, balance and stability of a stork, and your hands should move like the wings of a bird. In self defence, your impact on the opponent should have the same force as a bird of prey impacting on the quarry at the end of its power dive.

Your steps should be taken like a cat, which feels the ground before it puts each foot down. Your level of attentiveness should be like that of

a cat about to pounce on a mouse, coiled and ready to spring. As soon as the cat senses that the mouse is about to move, it pounces, claws extended and back arched as it makes the offensive movement. In Tai Chi, you do the same: extend your fingers and arch your back as you attack.

Cats lie down with their tails touching their noses. This behaviour shows the universal nature of the internal Chi Kung exercise known as the Small Circulation of Chi (*see page* 62).

◀ Crane cools wings from the Old Yang Style Long Form

Both Tai Chi and Chi Kung draw some of their knowledge from the observation of wild animals. But mostly, they have developed through the observation of people.

What will I experience?

People who practise Tai Chi experience Chi energy flowing through their meridians. When Chi flows around the body it feels like a warm electric glow. Aches or pains will occur wherever the Chi flow is blocked or stagnant: for example in areas where physical tension has built up owing to daily mental tension, or at the sites of health problems or old injuries.

Whatever the causes, these areas are eventually cleared as the Chi flow increases. As stagnant Chi is pushed out of the system, you may experience a dull mental nausea, but once it has cleared you will feel mentally clear and sharp and physically healed and strong.

When Chi tries to break through a blocked area, mild shaking occurs, which stops when the blockage is cleared.

When the body starts to shake more violently, this indicates complete exhaustion. If this occurs, stop training, have a big hot meal and a rest.

The third type of shaking is a humming vibration in the body, which feels like the sound a bumble bee makes and is very beneficial. It happens when the Chi is flowing smoothly through all the meridians and a person is in good health.

Unexpressed emotions accumulated over time are occasionally pushed to the surface by the increased Chi flow during training. When this happens, it is best to let them out rather than suppress them again. If they are not released, they will block the Chi flow, which could lead to illness developing at a later time: it is well known that emotional and physiological pressure (stress) can cause heart attacks and stomach ulcers. If shouting or crying occur, anger and sadness are being released. When these emotions have been cleared it is not unusual to find yourself gently laughing.

The lovely healing feeling of good Chi flowing during practice can also cause spontaneous gentle laughing. Practitioners also feel a tingling and fullness in their fingertips and other parts of the body.

When a meridian is activated you can feel its line of force through the body. At first you become more aware of the muscles, tendons and bones. Eventually Chi flows through the meridians more and more strongly, until you feel that your body is made up entirely of energy.

When you have practised for a few years, you feel as if an electromagnetic force field is building up around the hands and body. You also have a sense of weightlessness, as if in zero gravity or moving through water. At the highest level it feels as if you are made of warm, electric, liquid mercury.

What are the benefits of Tai Chi?

Tai Chi training brings many benefits, including: toned muscles; improved posture when both still and moving; better balance and coordination; greater self awareness; and increased wellbeing. The stress release and relaxation response created by Tai Chi also help general health and peace of mind.

Tai Chi movements encourage Chi to flow through the acupuncture meridians of the body and clear any blockages, to maintain good health. If you suffer from cold hands and feet, they will become warmer as your circulation improves.

At the end of each training session, the energy generated is stored in the Lower Tan Tien energy centre*(*see over*). As time goes by, you accumulate more and more energy, which strengthens your resistance to disease and provides a reserve which can be called upon in times of need.

The increase in energy from practising Tai Chi can heal not only the body but also the emotions. Often a person with a tendency towards feeling anxious or down and lacking self confidence has insufficient Chi energy. When you cultivate energy, you feel more substantial, confident and resilient.

If you suffer from non-specific aches and pains you will find that these clear up and re-occur less, because you have more internal strength to cope with the pressures in your life and so do not get so run down.

By training Tai Chi we become substantial and strong inside, because Tai Chi nourishes and strengthens not just the muscles and bones, but also the internal organs. Ultimately, the internal organs decide our strength and health.

When you have been training Tai Chi for a while, your general health will improve, you will catch colds and flu less often, get fewer aches and pains, and have a greater sense of well-being overall.

The benefits of Tai Chi result from regular practice over a long period of time. Occasionally magical things do happen but it is better to concentrate on regular daily training than to hope for a quick miracle.

* The Lower Tan Tien is a major energy centre located just below and behind the navel. The Middle Tan Tien is located behind the solar plexus and the Upper Tan Tien behind the point between the eyebrows. Although the Middle and Upper Tan Tiens are used in advanced Tai Chi, for the first few years beginners concentrate on the Lower Tan Tien, so that they develop a low centre of gravity, mental balance and stability.

Getting Started

How do I choose a teacher?

A good teacher should know and be able to teach the Ten Points of Correct Tai Chi Posture, the Ten Internal Principles of Tai Chi, and the Ten Methods of Practice of Tai Chi.

He should also be happy to answer any questions the students have about Tai Chi. If he has good communication skills, is able to create a good atmosphere in the class, and has a sense of humour, that is even better.

If you find a teacher with great vitality and ability, learn the techniques that he used to gain them, and develop them within yourself. A teacher is there to learn from, not to follow, so learn from him but follow yourself. A good teacher should not want people always looking to him; he should want people to look to themselves. The two best online resources for finding a Tai Chi teacher near you are www.taiji.net and www.taijiworld.com.

Training in a class

In a Tai Chi class, take the opportunity to train with as many different people as possible. Training with people of different heights and weights gives you the chance to develop a greater variety of responses. For example, when facing an opponent of much bigger build, you need speed and flexibility to cope with the longer reach and greater weight. If your opponent is shorter than you, he will have a lower centre of gravity, so you need to develop the ability to be rooted and stable in order not to be unbalanced by him.

   Training with others increases your sensitivity to the point where on contact with an opponent, you can tell his intention. Our intention rides on our energy, which extends to the skin's surface, so when you make contact (e.g. in Pushing Hands), your energy contacts theirs and you can read their intention.

   At the most advanced level of Tai Chi, you can develop the ability to conceal your intention from the opponent, while extending your Chi field beyond your body, so that you can sense their intention before you make contact with them. These skills take many years to develop.

Training on your own

As well as training in a class twice or three times a week, you should train by yourself every day. The benefits of Tai Chi are cumulative: it is better to do a little every day, rather than a lot one day, then nothing for a week.

Most classes are taught inside, but you should take every opportunity to practise outside. The fresh air and calm surroundings can help you attain a deeper meditative state.

Some wonderful experiences can be had when training outdoors. It is possible to send your energy into the ground, like the roots of a tree, and exchange energy with the Earth. This heals both physically and spiritually.

Often, as the energy in your body increases, you see nature in a new way: the colours of the flowers and trees become brighter; birdsong becomes clearer. Most wonderful of all, as your energy expands and blends with the energy of the natural world, you can connect and interact with the greater spirit of nature, of which we are all a part.

Do not train outdoors if it is too cold, hot, damp or windy, as these elemental factors can aggravate or cause illness.

When and for how long should I train?

Some practitioners believe that dawn and dusk are good times to train, when the Chi is changing between Yin night and Yang day. Others say that the Yin Yang changes at midday and midnight make these good times to practise. In keeping with the Taoist philosophy of 'easy and natural is right', you can, of course, do it whenever you feel like it.

The amount of time spent training each day will vary from person to person depending on their health and enthusiasm. It should be more than 15 minutes and not longer than six hours.

What should I wear?

No special clothing is required for Tai Chi: you do not need silk pyjamas or black baggy trousers. Wear what you like as long as it does not constrict your movement or blood flow. It is especially important not to wear a tight belt around your waist, or a wristwatch.

For better posture and rooting, wear flat-soled shoes, rather than heeled or running shoes. Many people wear Chinese slippers, but I find that boating shoes are more sturdy and durable.

It is highly beneficial to practise Tai Chi barefoot on the grass so that you can draw up Earth energy through the first point on the Kidney meridian, the Bubbling Spring, on the sole of the foot.

Is Tai Chi safe?

Only train at your own level and always consult a teacher to make sure you are practising your Tai Chi or Chi Kung correctly. This book is for reference only and cannot take the place of correct instruction from a competent teacher.

As long as beginners only do beginner level techniques they will be safe. If they try intermediate techniques before they are ready, they may cause themselves some harm. If they attempt advanced level techniques they could get seriously hurt, with unbalanced physical health and mental disharmony resulting. It is important not to push the body beyond what it is comfortable doing; the aim is to train to the point of exhilaration, not exhaustion. Tai Chi is not about having an excess of energy, but the maximum amount evenly distributed and well balanced. The aim is to feel vibrant and vitalized, not burned out.

In the section on Chi Kung, I explain how to balance energy in the body and store it safely in the Lower Tan Tien. If these guidelines are followed then there should be no problems with your energy or health.

Tai Chi is a lifetime's work. Progress is gradual and over a long period of time. It is not about forcing things to happen, but about training and training, and allowing them to happen when the time is right.

The Ten Points of Correct Tai Chi Posture

There are many different styles of Tai Chi, each of which has a slightly different emphasis. However, they all stress the importance of correct posture.

i The Feet Claw the Ground

Whenever your feet make contact with the ground, claw them slightly. This helps to develop rooting and activates the first point on the Kidney meridian (K–1), through which you can exchange energy with the Earth to heal yourself and others, and make a deeper spiritual connection with nature. To be activated, K-1 must be off the ground.

ii The Knees are Bent

Whether you practise Tai Chi in a low or a high stance, always keep the knees slightly bent, as though you are about to sit down. Avoid putting too much stress on the knee joints by making sure that the knees are not bent further than the toes. If the knees pass the toes, your body weight goes into the knees; as long as they do not pass the toes, your body weight is supported by the legs, and by the feet pressing into the ground.

This position creates a slight flex in the leg tendons, which draws Chi down the corresponding meridians, ensuring a strong circulation of Chi, blood and nutrients to the legs. It also encourages the development of internal power in the legs. If your legs are strengthened, you can continue to be active in old age.

Having the knees slightly bent helps activate the Lower Tan Tien energy centre, gives you a lower centre of gravity, and greater stability.

The only time the legs are locked straight in Tai Chi is during some of the kicks. This flexes the tendons that run down the backs of the legs and draws the Chi down their corresponding meridians.

The body should be aligned so that there is a vertical line between the acupuncture point on the top of the head (called Governing meridian 20) and the point on the top of the foot (known as Stomach meridian 41).

iii Acupuncture Point CV1 is Activated

The CV1 point is in the perineum and by pulling it up on inhalation it helps to pump the energy and essence up the spine into the head to energize the brain.

iv The Spine is Straight and Vertical

To straighten the upper spine, we lift the head back and up, and pull the chin in slightly. To straighten the lower spine, we tilt the coccyx forward and under the torso; this should happen naturally when the knees are bent.

To stretch the spine along its length, imagine a string attached to the back of the head pulling up, and a weight attached to the lower spine pulling down.

If the spine is straight and vertical while you perform the rotating, spiralling movements of Tai Chi, its flexibility is increased. The flow of spinal fluid and the function of the spinal nerves are unhindered, and Chi can ascend up the centre of the spine, through the Governing meridian, to the head.

By keeping the spine healthy, you reduce the likelihood of developing lumbago, sciatica, prolapsed discs and other back problems.

v The Tongue is on the Roof of the Mouth

Put the tongue on the roof of the mouth at the front, just like when you say the letter L.

Keep the tongue in this position while you practise Tai Chi forms, most Chi Kung, and meditation. It allows the Chi that has risen up the Governing meridian and over the top of the head, to connect with the Conception meridian, and descend down the front of the body into the belly. This circulation of energy is commonly known as the Small Circulation of Chi, and with each Tai Chi move, the energy completes one orbit.

If your tongue is not connected with the roof of the mouth, energy accumulates in the head instead of travelling down to the belly. It is important never to leave excess energy in the brain. Trapped Chi here could cause headaches and excessive mental activity. Neither should excess Chi be left in the heart, as it could cause excessive emotional states. Only by bringing the Chi down to the belly can you be balanced and stable.

If saliva accumulates in your mouth, swallow it, as it helps carry the vital essence and energy down to the belly.

The only times the tongue does not touch the roof are during Fa Jing explosive moves with a shout, and a few special Chi Kung exercises.

vi The Shoulders are Relaxed and Down

Allow your shoulders to relax and sink down, slightly forward. This stops the shoulders, neck and upper back from storing mental and physical tension, and allows Chi to sink into the belly.

vii The Elbows are Lower than the Shoulders

If your elbows are below shoulder-level, it is easier for the shoulders to remain relaxed and down. This helps the Chi to sink from the head and chest into the belly to give a lower centre of gravity.

viii The Armpits have a Space under them

You should always have a space under the armpits about the size of a football, so that energy can flow freely through the shoulder joints and down the arms. If the undersides of the arms are touching the torso, the shoulder joint is closed and the Chi flow to the hands is reduced.

ix The Arms Maintain a Circular Shape

Extend the arms in front of the body, but don't quite lock the elbows.

◀ Single Whip Posture
from the Old Yang
Style Form

They should not be too bent, however, because this reduces the Chi flow, in the same way that bending a hosepipe stops the water from flowing. Stretch the arms forward until you feel them connected across the upper back and they form, horizontally, the shape of an archer's bow, or a horseshoe, or as if you are hugging a large tree.

x The Hands are Slightly Flexed and Concave

Flex the tendons in the hands slightly as if you are reaching out to grab someone, but relax the muscles. The flex draws Chi down the meridians that correspond to the tendons, so you feel a fullness in your fingertips. The fingers should not be touching each other. The hands are concave so that you can hold the Chi in your palm. This posture activates the eighth point on the Pericardium meridian, which is used to emit Chi for both the martial and healing arts of Tai Chi.

Hold the thumb away from the other fingers; the web of skin between the index finger and thumb should be stretched.

The martial reason for having the fingers flexed and extended is that they develop great strength with the increased Chi flow; eventually, they become like steel daggers and can be used to stab an opponent. Powerful hands and fingers capable of emitting a concentrated flow of Chi also increase one's healing ability when treating a patient.

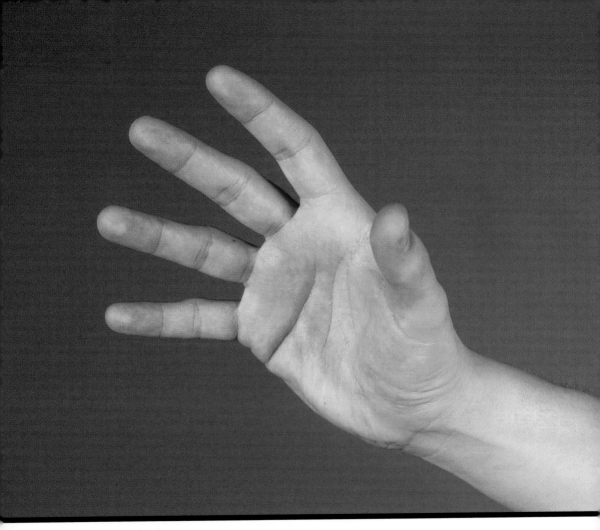

▲ Correct hand posture

The Ten Internal Principles of Tai Chi

Once you have mastered the correct posture, you can start to concentrate on some of the other internal aspects of Tai Chi.

i Circular and Spiralling Movement

All Tai Chi movements are circular and spiralling. Turning the waist from side to side generates centripetal and centrifugal forces which flow through the body causing the wrists and hands to spiral inwards (Yin) and outwards (Yang).

  The spiralling, twisting movements of the torso, and the subtle rotations of the joints make the whole body flow like a great river, and the energy spirals up and down around the arms, legs and torso. Even the punches have a slight corkscrew action.

Practised slowly, the movements are like a whirlpool; practised fast, they are like a whirlwind. When you execute a series of Fa Jing explosive movements, you become a cyclone of spiralling power: calm in the centre, but outwardly manifesting an unstoppable force.

ii Slowness and Smoothness

Beginners practise Tai Chi slowly. Continuous, smooth, slow, flowing movement encourages Chi to flow in a very healing way. To develop the flow, go through the Tai Chi form once; a second time at half the speed; then a third time, at half that speed. Eventually you will be moving so slowly, with so much energy, that it will feel like walking on the moon.

Yang Lu Chan's Old Yang style of Tai Chi has Fa Jing explosive movements evenly interspersed between slow movements. This is a good way of maintaining balance in the body: slow movements are Yin, and Fa Jing movements are Yang. You move at a continuous smooth, slow, flowing rate, perform a sudden explosive Fa Jing, then move slowly and smoothly again.

By practising slowly, you enter into a meditative state, and the conscious programming of the subconscious with the Tai Chi moves and their self-defence applications is made easier. You also develop the ability to perform the moves without muscle tension, so that later you can perform them as Fa Jing effectively. If you try to Fa Jing without being relaxed, you can tear muscles.

iii Relaxation and Sinking (Sung)

Sung means letting go of unnecessary tension in your body and mind, relaxing and sinking into the Tai Chi posture. If you let go of physical tension, it is easier to let go of mental tension. When the body is Sung, the mind can be Sung, and vice versa.

When Sung, your body becomes more supple, elastic and resilient and there is more Chi (energy) and Jing (internal power). In Sung, you are at ease and alert, calm and focused. Sung means to move without feeling the movements.

To achieve Sung, first let go of all tension in the shoulders, so they can sink down and slightly forward; then let go of the tensed, high-held chest, and allow it to relax and sink down – then you can let go of your clenched jaw and even smile! Next, allow your tensed, held-in belly to relax and expand so the Chi can gather there. It is possible to move without tension: tension restricts the flow of blood and Chi and makes movements slow and clumsy. Though the muscles are relaxed, all the tendons in the body are slightly flexed.

Some people think a soldier has good posture: shoulders back, chest out and belly in. Sung is the opposite: shoulders forward, chest in and belly out!

All Tai Chi is done with mental intention, not muscle tension. Even at the point of impact there is no muscular tension. When Sung, your centre of gravity is lower, so that physically and mentally you are more stable and balanced.

iv Rooting

Rooting comes from the lower half of the body and its contact with the ground. Once this power-base has been developed, the internal force generated can be transferred to the upper body.

To develop rooting, physically sink your body weight, and imagine that it is mainly in your lower belly and legs, not in your chest and head.

Grip the ground with your feet like claws, while pushing the legs against the ground and each other. As you shift your body weight from leg to leg, one expands and the other compresses. Like springs, each leg stores and releases its coiled energy.

Don't let the body rise up as you shift from leg to leg, because the internal power generated will be dissipated. Pushing from the legs turns the hips, waist and belly from side to side.

So rooting is a combination of several things: firstly, sinking the body weight into the lower body, legs and feet by physically sinking and being Sung; secondly, clawing the ground with the feet; thirdly, pushing the leg against the ground; and fourthly, pushing the legs against each other like springs storing and releasing their power.

v Centrifugal Waist Power

The rooting power from the Earth and the legs is controlled by the waist and belly, which turn the torso from side to side. This rotation transfers the internal force from the lower to the upper body.

Because of the weight and bulk of the waist and belly, the movement generates a great deal of centrifugal and centripetal force. Used correctly, tremendous power can be generated in a very small space. With Fa Jing, the vigorous turn and recoil of the waist sends the hands flying out and back with explosive force.

Here is a Tai Chi warm-up technique that demonstrates this principle. Stand with your feet shoulder-width apart, knees slightly bent, your spine straight and vertical. Keep your feet stuck to the floor and turn your waist to the right and left.

Carry on with this manoeuvre, keeping the upper body relaxed and loose as you turn from side to side, remembering to stay level. The arms are thrown outward by the centrifugal force; their movement contains great power but is totally effortless.

When incorporated into a Tai Chi form, centrifugal waist power increases the circulation of blood and Chi to the extremities without straining the heart. The rotating and twisting massages all the internal organs, increasing their Chi and essence, and encouraging these to flow through the meridian system like water released from a reservoir flowing down a river.

To develop centrifugal and centripetal waist power, go through the whole form very slowly and move the waist half a second before the rest of the body moves. Once this principle has been grasped, the hands, feet and waist appear to move at the same time.

The waist turn can also happen without the push from the legs, in fact you can Fa Jing as you fly through the air. At a high level the Fa Jing of the waist moves the feet in the same way it moves the hands.

vi Uniting the Lower and Upper Body

A lot of power is generated by moving the lower body (hips, waist and belly) slightly ahead of the upper body (the ribcage). If the movement is disjointed, the torque power from this counter-movement is lost; so don't over-emphasize it. Moving the lower body a moment before the upper body massages the thoracic diaphragm and internal organs.

When the lower and upper body are united, there is little or no time delay between the development of internal power in the legs and waist and its release from the hands.

There are three ways to help unification: firstly, position the nose directly above the navel, so that the head moves with the body; secondly, match the movement of the elbows to that of the hips, so that if the left hip bone moves forward or backward, the left elbow does too. The same applies to the right side. Thirdly and most importantly, try to keep the hands on your centre line – this is an imaginary line running down the front of the torso from the nose to the navel. If the hands ever leave this position, it should only be by a few centimetres, then they should return immediately. This is very important for self defence

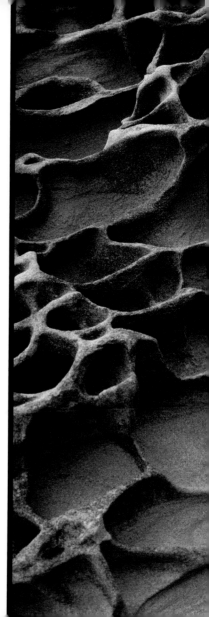

Tai Chi: if your hands remain on your centre line, you can deflect your opponent's attack away from your centre as you attack his centre.

vii Internal Force (Jing)

Jing is a type of heavy, loose, relaxed, elastic whole body power which is different from localized stiff muscle power. To best understand Jing, think of the difference between an axeman chopping down a tree, and a carpenter hammering in a nail. The axeman uses his whole body in an integrated way, using his waist rotation, leg power and his arms for each stroke, whereas the carpenter uses only his arm each time he strikes.

Normal physical strength comes from the muscles expanding and contracting. Jing comes from the development of elasticity and resilience in the tendons (the connective tissue between the muscles and bones) and the sinews, which are the connective tissues between the bones in the joints.

When you practise Tai Chi, relax the muscles so that Chi can flow unimpeded around the body and nourish the tendons. The flex in the tendons attracts Chi; as a result they become elastic and strong. The tendons form a latticework from the tips of the fingers to the tips of the toes and the top of the head, and the whole body becomes a unit of dynamic, elastic power.

Jing gives Tai Chi self-defence techniques more power. The great force that a Tai Chi practitioner can deliver in his Fa Jing palm strike or punch is because of his internal force, his Jing.

The movements of people who don't let go of their muscle tension are like dead, brittle branches. Those who completely relax both their muscles and tendons move like limp grass that bends in the wind. In Tai Chi, you strive for balance. You don't want to be too hard (Yang) or too soft (Yin); you want to be flexible and resilient like young bamboo, so that when the wind blows, you bend, then spring back.

Jing gives you a spring in your step and a vitality to your body. As you get older you will stay flexible and active if you develop your Jing.

viii Connection

Being connected means that each part of the body is attached to and moved by a part that has moved just before, so that the rhythm of movement is like a wave through the body, like the flowing connection of a snake. Each movement begins in the feet (which push against the ground), rises up through the legs (which push against each other), which then rotate the waist, which turns the spine, which turns the ribcage. You then feel the arm connect to the ribcage and be moved. The hands follow last of all. The wave-like transference of internal force through the body should be smooth and fluid.

To develop connection, imagine that your whole body is moving through the air as if it were under water. Eventually your movements seem to be effortless. In beginners, the time delay as power is transferred through the body is obvious; in advanced practitioners it is not perceptible, and every part appears to move at once.

ix Avoiding Double-weightedness

The Yin-Yang balance in Tai Chi should be dynamic, otherwise the movements become double-weighted. This means that the flow is not natural, like water in a canal rather than water in a river. In Tai Chi, every part of the body is moving. Never over-extend or under-extend your movements: rotate and twist in a dynamic, balanced way.

It is most important to avoid double-weightedness in the feet and in the hands.

x Integration

Integration means doing the Ten Points of Correct Posture, the Ten Internal Principles, and the Ten Methods of Practice of Tai Chi at the same time.

The Ten Methods of Practice of Tai Chi

The differences in how Tai Chi is practised are to do with your level of development, which I have categorized in this book as beginner, intermediate and advanced.

Tai Chi has no harmful side effects when practised correctly. Never try to force things to happen; instead, relax, and let things happen in their own time. Be patient, persevere, and you will develop slowly and surely.

i Stance

Beginner
Beginners have weak legs, so they start in a high stance. As their strength increases, they can make their stance lower.

Intermediate

Intermediate level practitioners using a low stance develop great strength in their legs and a lower centre of gravity, the root of power for applying Tai Chi.

Advanced

At this level, practitioners have internalized their ability and can generate great internal force in the legs from an almost normal standing stance. The knees are still a little bent.

A low centre of gravity is achieved at this level by being mentally sunk into the belly and legs.

ii Posture

Beginner

Beginners concentrate on changing their S-shaped spines to straight and vertical.

Intermediate

Intermediates have a C-shaped back, like a cat about to pounce on a mouse.

Advanced

Advanced practitioners have a straight, vertical spine physically, but the energetic feeling of a C-shape.

iii Mental State

Beginner

In Tai Chi, the best way to progress is not to try and make things happen, but to let them happen. Trying to relax creates tension; you have to allow yourself to relax.

Intermediate

Intermediate level practitioners understand that Tai Chi is more experiential than intellectual. They are not in their heads, they are in their bellies: centred, balanced and calm. They are just getting on with

the training and experiencing the flow and transformation of Chi within themselves. The conscious mind is no longer chattering, it is calm and quiet.

Advanced

Advanced level practitioners let the Tai Chi do itself. They do not have their conscious minds present to get in the way and, as a result, they have lightning reflexes.

iv Breathing

Beginner

Beginners keep the chest and belly relaxed and do not think about their breathing. They keep a part of their attention in the Lower Tan Tien in the lower belly, to help the Chi gather there. From the Lower Tan Tien, a major energy centre, the Chi can flow to all other parts of the body.

Intermediate

Intermediate students use Upper Abdominal Breathing which strengthens the acquired Chi (Chi from food and air). The chest stays relaxed and down. Inhale while moving the hands down or towards the body, and allow the area between the solar plexus and the navel to expand. Exhale while moving the hands up or away from the body, and allow the area between the solar plexus and the navel to contract. This breathing is accomplished by mental intention, not by muscle tension. Do not force anything; keep the mouth closed, and breathe through the nose slowly and calmly.

Advanced

Advanced level practitioners use Reverse Lower Abdominal breathing, which strengthens inherited Chi (the Chi you were born with). Inhale while moving the hands down or toward the body, and allow the area between the navel and the pubic bone to contract. Exhale while moving the hands up or away from the body, and allow the same area to expand.

Keep your mouth closed and breathe through the nose. Each breath should be calm, deep and slow, not forced but allowed to happen by itself. The body movements are totally integrated with the breathing, which should be so quiet that even you cannot hear it.

v Eyes

Beginners

When doing the solo forms, beginners watch the horizon with a calm expression. This helps keep your head upright and allows you to relax. Occasionally doing the whole form with your eyes closed helps to develop internal balance and improve your sense of direction.

Intermediate

When doing the solo forms, intermediate level practitioners watch the space where the opponent would be.

This use of focus vision connects your movements with your conscious mind. If during training you visualize yourself applying the moves against imaginary opponents, you are consciously programming them into your subconscious.

Advanced

At this level, move the eyes so that the hands are always in the area of your peripheral vision. Peripheral vision connects with the subconscious mind and this has two benefits.

Firstly, because the subconscious is activated and thinks that you really are going to do the martial applications of Tai Chi, a great amount of Chi is released. Because you are not using this Chi against an opponent, it rushes around your body, healing imbalances and improving your health.

Secondly, when applying Tai Chi in self defence, because the subconscious has been programmed with all the Tai Chi moves and applications, and is several hundred times faster at responding than the conscious mind, you have a greater chance of defeating the opponent.

vi Hand Circles and Waist Rotation

Beginner

Beginners should make large, expressive hand circles and waist rotations, to release physical and mental tension and open up their meridians.

The waist moves first, then a split second later the hands move. This is so that the centrifugal and centripetal waist power is correctly transferred to the hands.

Intermediate

Intermediate students have learned how to let go of physical and mental tension, so they no longer need such expansive movements, and can make their waist rotations and corresponding hand circles smaller. They have less external physical movement and more internal energetic movement.

Advanced

Advanced practitioners imagine doing large movements but actually only do very small movements. The circles become so small that almost nothing appears to be happening, but internally there is a massive movement of energy and the creation of tremendous power. Like a big spring compressed into a small box, we have huge potential energy, which is released in Fa Jing.

vii Fa Jing – an Explosive Movement

Beginner

Beginners do not practise Fa Jing. They practise doing the Tai Chi moves slowly, without muscle tension, to build up their Chi. You can only practise Fa Jing when you have no muscle tension in the body.

Intermediate

Intermediate students begin tentatively to practise Fa Jing as a conscious action. To Fa Jing, vigorously shake your waist: the shake travels through the whole body. By the time it reaches the hands and feet the force is concentrated, so your punch or kick has great power. The waist goes left right left or right left right to make one basic Fa Jing movement.

Advanced

Advanced level practitioners do Fa Jing in all the different areas of Tai Chi. They have an excess of Chi that they need to release.

At an advanced level, the release of Chi can be so great that you get 'blown away' – you temporarily lose your sense of self, not just on Fa Jing moves but during the whole form. Great healing can occur, because you are not 'there' to get in the way.

Fa Jing is a sudden, whole-body shaking movement during which you exhale, push the lower abdomen out and vigorously turn the waist so that the hands are thrown out while you shout. The recoil of the waist takes you into the next Fa Jing.

In training, Fa Jing has great healing power, and in the martial applications of Tai Chi it has a devastating effect on the opponent.

Tai Chi's slow movements build up the Chi, and Fa Jing explosive movements release the excess. Slow movements without Fa Jing are like Yin without Yang: unbalanced.

The most advanced type of Fa Jing is when a shockwave of energy rushes through the body causing the hands to vibrate.

viii Opening and Closing

Beginner

Beginners do not include special breathing in their training and are unaware of Opening and Closing.

Intermediate

Intermediate students are told which moves are Open and which are Closed but the technique is not fully explained to them. They are using upper abdominal breathing.

Advanced

Advanced level practitioners use Reverse Lower Abdominal Breathing and are shown how to use Opening and Closing with each Tai Chi move. Opening and Closing is breathing not just with the belly, but with the whole body. They are small, internal movements not perceptible to an observer.

   To Open and Close means to bend and straighten the two bows of the body in conjunction with Reverse Lower Abdominal Breathing.

   The Horizontal Arm Bow is a line from the tip of your middle finger, up the outside of the arm, across the back, and down the outside of the other arm to the tip of the middle finger on the other hand. The Vertical Spine Bow is a single line from the coccyx up the spine to the crown of the head. When the bows are straight, the hands apart, the

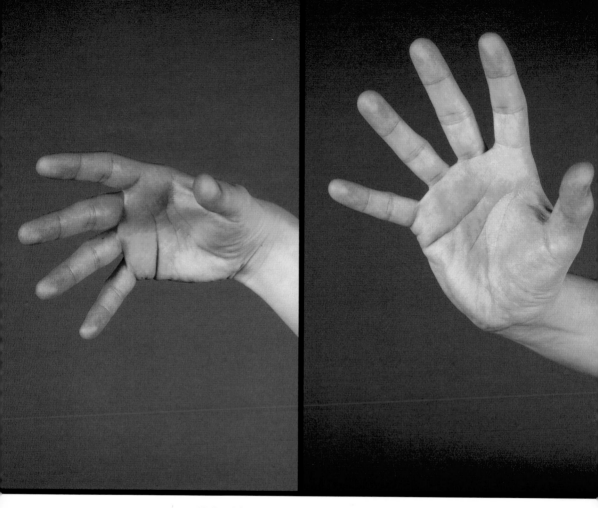

Yin hand ▲ ▲ Yang hand

spine straight and the breath and the lower belly in, you are Opening. When the bows are bent, the hands slightly closer together, the spine curved like a crescent moon, and the breath and lower belly out, you are Closing.

ix Yin Yang Changes

Beginner
Beginners concentrate on the Yin Yang changes in the legs: storing and releasing internal power, and shifting the body weight from leg to leg.

Intermediate
Intermediate students concentrate on the Yin Yang change of the waist turning from side to side. The centrifugal and centripetal waist power is a result of the push from the legs: the leg pushes, the waist turns, the hand is thrown out to hit the target. You do not punch through the target, nor do you punch and stop on impact: the centrifugal Yang and centripetal Yin energies mean that you punch and pull back to give a penetrating, percussive blow to the opponent. This Yin Yang waist recoil action can happen independently of the leg power.

Advanced
Advanced practitioners use the Yin and Yang changes of the legs, waist and Opening and Closing movements.

The most advanced Yin Yang change is in the hands: a continual flow between a Yang palm and a Yin palm. Neither are ever one hundred per cent Yin or Yang; there is always transformation from one to the other.

The Yin-Yang palm changes store and release Chi. As the hand releases its Yang Chi it accumulates Yin Chi, and vice versa.

As your ability develops, a very powerful Chi density builds up in and around the hands, which feels like an electromagnetic force field.

x Internalization

Beginner
Beginners concentrate on internalizing the Ten Points of Correct Tai Chi Posture, so that they can go from being in their normal posture to being in the Tai Chi posture without appearing to have changed in any way. This is useful because if you find yourself in a potentially violent situation, you want to be ready to respond, but you do not want to provoke an attack by making an obvious offensive movement. Tai Chi's fighting stance looks like a normal standing stance.

From the Old Yang Style of Tai Chi. Part of a sequence called ▶
'Sleeves Dancing like Plum Blossom'

Intermediate

Intermediate students concentrate on internalizing the Ten Internal Principles and the Ten Methods of Practice of Tai Chi. You use all these abilities which are now under your subconscious control, and do not have to be consciously initiated. Only an experienced observer can tell what you are doing. A passer-by might notice that there was something going on but would not be able to say what it was.

Advanced

At this level, things happen that are hard to convey and are best understood by personally experiencing them. You are no longer just your body or your Chi, your subconscious or your conscious: you are also your superconscious – your spirit.

By becoming so internalized you trigger an equal and opposite occurrence, and your spirit is externalized: you are inside and outside yourself at the same time, and can shift your awareness to your spirit body.

At this level you attain the Wu Chi way of perceiving the world. The Tai Chi way of perceiving is the normal, everyday reality – the physical world – where everything is dualistic: there is always a subject–object relationship in which things are judged as good or bad, and time is linear.

When you perceive the Wu Chi way, there is no duality, no subject or object, because you realize how everything is part of everything else.

Good and bad are no longer fixed, they fluctuate as circumstances change. Time is no longer a one-way journey: the relationship between the past, present and future changes in the most mysterious and interesting ways.

Tai Chi is the Yin-Yang diagram; Wu Chi is symbolized by an empty circle.

To be balanced, a Tai Chi practitioner must be comfortable and confident in both realities. He must be able to move from one to the other at will, and to exist in both simultaneously.

Tai Chi and Wu Chi flow into one another and together comprise the Tao (the Way, *see page* 88). Each person is Tai Chi and Wu Chi simultaneously: each person is Tao.

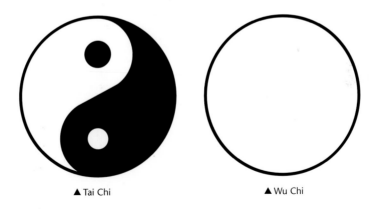

▲ Tai Chi   ▲ Wu Chi

Chi Kung

Chi Kung means exercises that work with energy, so Tai Chi is a type of Chi Kung.

In this chapter, two Chi Kung exercises are explained, which are often practised within Tai Chi: the Basic Chi Kung Standing Posture and the Small Circulation of Chi. Both help to increase energy, improve health and balance the mind and emotions. They are usually practised before a training session as a warm up and afterwards as a cool down, but can also be practised independently.

The Basic Chi Kung Standing Posture

To do the Basic Chi Kung Standing Posture, stand with your feet a little more than shoulder-width apart, and your hands in front of you as if hugging a large tree. Use the Ten Points of Correct Posture, keep the hands at neck height, and be Sung, so that greater amounts of Chi can flow and more Jing can be developed.

Hold the posture for 15 minutes every morning as soon as you wake up. The posture activates the Chi in the Lower Tan Tien and releases it into the body so that it reaches the ends of the fingers and toes and the top of the head. You will experience Chi energy flowing through the meridians like a warm electric glow. You may also feel a tingling and fullness in the fingertips and other parts of the body.

The Small Circulation of Chi

The Small Circulation of Chi takes the Chi from the Lower Tan Tien, under the torso, up the spine through the Governing meridian, over the top of the head and then down the front of the body along the Conception meridian and back into the Lower Tan Tien. The Governing and Conception meridians can store more Chi than any of the other meridians, and circulating the Chi through them helps to fill them up.

The Chi is led through the Small Circulation by your intention: your strength of will takes the Chi from point to point around the body. Although you can use breathing to help move Chi, you should not be dependent on it. With experience, the channels open fully and the Chi flows freely through them almost effortlessly. It makes one full circulation in each Tai Chi movement.

The Small Circulation of Chi is usually practised in the Basic Chi Kung Standing Posture but it can also be practised while sitting down. In the Standing Posture, begin by smiling down to the Lower Tan Tien to activate your energy with a positive intention. Try to keep your mind empty. If you can't, think positive things.

When you feel Chi in the Lower Tan Tien, bring it forward to C– 4 (see diagram) and down to the sexual organs, the perineum C–1, the anus sphincter muscle and G–1 at the coccyx.

Then take it up through the centre of the spine along G– 4, G– 6, G –11, G –14, G –16 in the occipital cavity and G–20 on the top of the head, then to the third eye (between the eyebrows), through the roof of the mouth to the tip of the tongue, down to the throat C–22, the chest C–17, the solar plexus C–12, the navel C– 8, and then C–6 back to C– 4, and from there back to the Lower Tan Tien.

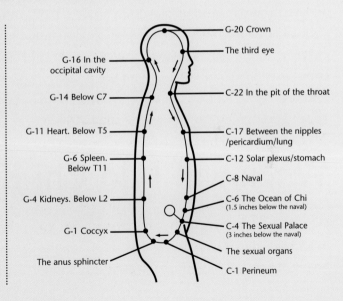

G= Governing meridian, runs up the centre of the back

C= Conception meridian, runs along the mid-line of the front of the body

C7= Cervical vertebra number seven

T5= Thoracic vertebra number five

T11= Thoracic vertebra number eleven

L2= Lumbar vertebra number two

G-16 In the occipital cavity

G-14 Below C7

G-11 Heart. Below T5

G-6 Spleen. Below T11

G-4 Kidneys. Below L2

G-1 Coccyx

The anus sphincter

G-20 Crown

The third eye

C-22 In the pit of the throat

C-17 Between the nipples /pericardium/lung

C-12 Solar plexus/stomach

C-8 Naval

C-6 The Ocean of Chi (1.5 inches below the naval)

C-4 The Sexual Palace (3 inches below the naval)

The sexual organs

C-1 Perineum

This is one circuit. To do more, instead of going from C–4 back to the Lower Tan Tien, continue straight on to the sexual organs and go round the circuit again, only returning to the Lower Tan Tien when you have done your final circuit.

Having completed three, six or nine orbits of the Small Circulation of Chi, store the Chi in the Lower Tan Tien by placing the palms over C–4 and concentrating on it while rubbing it gently for a minute. When the Chi is in the Lower Tan Tien, the belly might feel more substantial, producing a calm, happy feeling. At this point, think positive things, like 'I feel balanced and calm deep down inside myself.' Or don't think, just be.

The Small Circulation of Chi helps to transform the Ching (vital essence) to Chi (vital energy) to Shen (spirit), and ensures that the Chi is more evenly distributed around the body.

Always finish Tai Chi, Chi Kung or meditation by bringing the Chi back to the Lower Tan Tien and storing it there.

When will I do Chi Kung?

A training session incorporating the two Chi Kung exercises described is structured in the following way.

First, spend 15 minutes in the Basic Chi Kung Standing Posture, doing circuits of the Small Circulation of Chi, and bring the Chi back to the Lower Tan Tien, not to store it but to centre yourself.

Now that the energy is activated you do your Tai Chi training: single and two-person forms, weapons, etc. Afterwards, you spend a few minutes in the Basic Chi Kung Standing Posture, and do three, six or nine circuits of the Small Circulation of Chi, then store the Chi in the Lower Tan Tien. Often, any excess energy radiates from the hands as a warm glow. This excess in the hands can be used for self-healing, for example, by placing them over your kidneys.

Over time, your Chi energy accumulates, and can be used for healing and to bring about positive changes in your life. If you are full of Chi you tend to be more cheerful.

Men place left palm on C4 below naval and other hand on ▶
top; for women right palm on belly and left on top

Tai Chi Weapons Forms

Tai Chi is a martial art. Although many people practise it today primarily for the great benefits it brings to the mind, body and spirit, the self-defense application of Tai Chi is still relevant. The weapons forms and fighting strategy explained below are key elements of Tai Chi as a martial art.

The weapons forms are usually taught when the empty hand forms have been learnt. They contain the Ten Points of Correct Posture, the Ten Internal Principles, and the Ten Methods of Practice of Tai Chi.

Tai Chi has several weapons forms, including the Long Sword and Dagger, the Single Sabre and Double Sabre, the Short Stick, Staff and Spear. The Walking Stick form is very useful for old people living in dangerous places, because they can have a weapon to defend themselves with, which is legal and does not attract attention.

In general, the short single weapons are taught first: Short Stick,

Walking Stick and Single Sabre. The double weapons forms come next: Double Sabre and the Sword and Dagger; and last are the long weapons forms, the Staff and the Spear.

All the weapons eventually feel as if they are a part of you, like an extra limb, and the Chi that emanates from you extends to the end of the weapon.

All the weapons forms at an advanced level contain Fa Jing.

When practising the weapons forms you must be Sung. The body releases more Chi to support the extra weight you are holding, and the increased Chi flowing round the body results in greater healing.

▼ Movements from the Tai Chi short stick form. We extend our energy into the weapon

Tai Chi Fighting Strategy

The fighting stance

The Tai Chi fighting stance looks like a normal standing stance, but internally all the correct Points of Posture, Internal Principles and Methods of Practice of Tai Chi have been automatically activated by your subconscious at the first hint of danger. The Tai Chi fighting stance does not provoke the opponent unnecessarily, which increases the chances of avoiding a confrontation. If your opponent makes the mistake of attacking you, you are ready to respond to any move.

Responses

Yin response to a Yin situation

In a Yin situation, there is very little chance of getting seriously hurt, for example, if the opponent is very weak or drunk. Use a Yin response such as a pushing or pulling technique and to subdue the opponent throw him away.

Yang response to a Yang situation

In a Yang situation, the opponent or opponents have every intention of seriously injuring or killing you. A Yang response is to use Fa Jing counterstrikes with the intention of stopping the opponent immediately. We only use Fa Jing and Dim Mak (acupuncture point striking) if our lives or the lives of our families and friends are in danger.

Yang response to a Yin situation

To use a Yang response in a Yin situation is unvirtuous. There is no benefit in such an act: causing unnecessary harm to others harms yourself. Only use Tai Chi's Yang responses when you have no choice.

Yin response to a Yang situation

To use a Yin response in a Yang situation may be thought of as correct moral behaviour, but the advantage it gives the opponent may lead to your defeat. Only a practitioner who has reached the peak of ability should use a Yin response in a Yang situation.

The Four Directions and Four Corners

Imagine you are standing in the middle of a compass, with north straight ahead, south behind, west to the left, and east to the right. These are the Four Directions.

Diagonally forward to the left is northwest, diagonally forward to the right is northeast, diagonally back to the left is southwest and diagonally back to the right is southeast. These are the Four Corners.

When an opponent attacks you, the best defence is attack, so moving to the northeast or northwest are the preferred directions because we are angling slightly out of the way of their attack as we move forwards. This way we are not where they are attacking and we can hit them from the side, or take one more step and hit them from behind.

Windows and Doors

Windows and Doors are metaphors for ways of getting through the opponent's defensive perimeter. For example, if he steps forward with his right foot and throws a straight right punch, you Fa Jing step forward with your left foot to the northwest, and your waist rotates to the right. The back (right) foot is moved slightly to the west by the force of the Fa Jing.

The Fa Jing centrifugal power of the waist rotation to the right throws the arms upward and out: at this point you are Opening. As you start to Close, your right hand hits the outside of your opponent's arm just above his right elbow, either to deflect the attacking arm, or damage the elbow. The final part is when the left hand hits either his head or exposed ribs.

The Three Distances

The use of the Eight Directions and Windows and Doors is possible if you know how to use the Three Distances. The first distance is Outside: here you are beyond the opponent's punching and kicking distance. Next is the Middle, where your and the opponent's limbs can impact with each other, but you are not close enough to hit his torso or his head. The last one is Inside: you are so close to him that you can hit his torso and head. If you stay Outside, the opponent cannot reach you. If he makes the mistake of attacking, thus giving you a Door, move as he moves and step through the Door. While passing through the Middle you control and deflect the opponent off your centre line and place yourself in a position to attack. Once inside, strike repeatedly and decisively.

Code of Virtuous Martial Conduct - Tai Chi Version

- Never attack first, because you do not want to open any Windows or Doors for the opponent to get Inside. Wait for him to make his offensive move, and as soon as he does, or you sense his intention to do so, counterattack.
- Tai Chi is for defence: when someone attacks you, defend yourself, using only the appropriate Yin or Yang response.
- Do not start fights and avoid known trouble spots: you are training to build yourself up rather than to bring others down.
- Train hard, but aim never to use Tai Chi in combat. If you become involved in a confrontation, try every possible means of avoiding a fight.

So if you practise Tai Chi but never use it for self defence, what is the point? Well, by practising Tai Chi daily, you end up being very healthy, happy and having a long life!

◀ Some Tai Chi movements have applications that we would not use in a fight. Their purpose is more to do with keeping the body flexible and strong

The Three Treasures

The Three Treasures have many strands, which intertwine to produce a tapestry of understanding about how our internal worlds and the external world relate to one another. All three exist simultaneously, integrated and continually transforming into one another. They can be divided into the following categories:

Physical World	Energy World	Spirit World
Ching (vital essence)	Chi (vital energy)	Shen (spirit)
Conscious Mind	Subconscious Mind	Superconscious Mind
Substance	Function	Intention
Physical Body	Energy Body	Spirit Body

The physical world, energy world and spirit world

Some people are only comfortable with the modern world of materialism. Others shun everyday life and devote themselves to the mysterious and ancient spirit world. The third way is not to see everyday life and spirituality as opposites, but to embrace both at the same time.

All the worlds overlap and interact, and are part of one another. A person is also a composite of spirit, energy and a physical body. When you realize this, the possibilities in your life open up and you are no longer limited by the laws of physical mechanics because you can tap into energy dynamics and vast spiritual forces.

It is possible to activate dormant senses through Tai Chi training, so that you perceive and experience the energy and spirit worlds. One example could be called 'seeing with the skin'. When your eyes are closed and you make contact with an opponent, you can still 'see' where he is and what he intends to do.

By experiencing the world of Chi inside you through the practice of Tai Chi and Chi Kung, it becomes possible to feel and interact with the Chi of other people.

Tai Chi and Chi Kung develop various natural abilities that we all have to a greater or lesser degree, for example, the ability to see energy or people who are no longer in their bodies, and non-human spirit entities, and the ability to channel energy through yourself to heal others.

It is vital that these natural abilities are only used to help and heal others. If you use them to control, manipulate or harm, then because of the dynamics of universal balance, you will be setting in motion a series of events that will eventually harm yourself.

Vital essence, vital energy and spirit

According to ancient Taoist theory there are three treasures within the body: Ching (vital essence), Chi (vital energy) and Shen (spirit).

When you practise Tai Chi, you transform vital essence into vital energy into spirit. The process of using up our essence (Ching) to give ourselves a functional power (Chi) so that we can carry out our intentions (Shen) is a natural one. It can be described symbolically in the following way.

Imagine a cauldron in the belly containing your Ching, the Elixir of Life. When the cauldron is heated, steam rises and permeates the whole body. The steam is Chi energy. On reaching the head, it condenses and rains back down into the cauldron in the belly to be reheated.When this process has been happening for a while, a very fine vapour-like energy collects in the head. This is Shen. The higher the level of Tai Chi, the more the processes of transformation and circulation are activated.

In old age, when less vital essence remains in the body, it can become like a tree with no sap. If you conserve your vital essence and train Tai Chi every day, then even in old age you will have a supple, resilient body, and remain healthy and active with a sound mind and strong spirit.

The conscious, subconscious and superconscious minds

The subconscious mind carries out various automatic functions and can store huge amounts of information. When you practise Tai Chi, and notice that your posture or hand–eye coordination is incorrect, you continually, consciously correct it. Eventually your posture is corrected and your hand–eye coordination improves. This is because you have consciously reprogrammed your subconscious.

While training Tai Chi and Chi Kung, the door between the conscious and subconscious is more open than usual, so it is a good time to reprogramme the subconscious with positive intentions.

Old patterns of behaviour and unresolved issues trap energy, which can be freed again for us to use. While clearing an issue, you may find emotions associated with it that have never been expressed. These need to be released: the suppressed emotion is an energy block, which if left might lead to illness developing.

Tai Chi calms the usually agitated conscious mind. This is the meditative aspect of Tai Chi that many people are familiar with. Don't try to meditate while doing Tai Chi: if you are doing it correctly, it just happens.

When the conscious mind is calm, mental and physical tension is released. Beginners use this relaxation response to release stress that they have accumulated during the day.

When the conscious mind is calm enough, enlightening insights from the superconscious can manifest themselves. If you practise Tai Chi regularly, you will spontaneously experience moments of deep insight

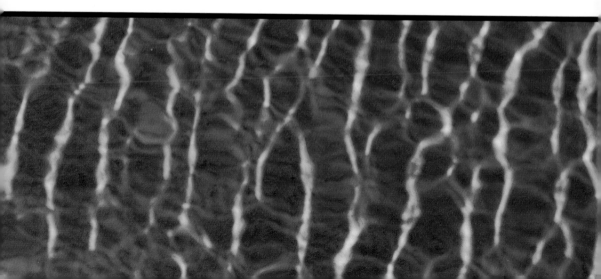

and clarity in everyday life. Eventually, the superconscious mind becomes a tangible voice in your head, giving clear, wise advice. As time goes by, all three minds become a single, clear awareness.

Substance, function and intention

The substance of the physical body has its functional activity powered by energy, and intention is the spiritual force that initiates everything.

Ice is a solid that can transform into liquid water, and into steam, which can rise up into the sky. Ice, water and steam are the same thing in different states; a person is much the same in relation to substance, function and intention.

In advanced Tai Chi training, you move in such a way that your body seems to melt and flow, and your spirit can ascend out of your body and you can look down at yourself doing Tai Chi. This is accomplished by doing Tai Chi with your intention. Intention is a spiritual force that must be cultivated if you are to achieve your highest objectives.

Lead your spirit body with your intention, and your physical body follows. Once you have done the move with the spirit, there is no need to repeat it with the physical body, so you go on to the next move: you do less with your physical body and more with your spirit body. Do the whole form in this way.

The internal development of your intention eventually enables you to externalize your spirit, and you watch from a slightly elevated position as your physical body goes through the Tai Chi form.

After many years of practice, you feel as familiar with your spirit body as you do with your physical body, and are able to fly in your spirit body as naturally as walking in your physical body.

At the time of death we must permanently leave our physical bodies. At a very advanced level of Tai Chi, the transition into spirit is familiar and the spirit world is a place you have visited many times, so you are able enjoyably to continue your journey of development and discovery in the great unlimited universe.

The physical body, the energy body and the spirit body

It is possible to strengthen your physical body so that it lasts long enough to develop an energy body, which can be transformed into an immortal spirit body. To attain this spiritual immortality, it is important to have a sensible life-style, a healthy diet and to practise Tai Chi and Chi Kung daily.

Understanding the Chi energy inside yourself is the key to unlocking the door to the spirit world. First, use your energy to strengthen your physical body, then fill up all the organs, Tan Tiens, and acupuncture meridians with Chi. Refine your Ching essence into Chi energy into Shen spirit, and use the spiritual energy to nourish and cultivate the spirit body inside you.

When you are ready, 'open the door' on the top of your head and rise up out of yourself into the spirit world.

By becoming familiar with the idea of existing outside your physical body, the fear of death is overcome. Knowing that death is not the end, but just a change of state, allows you to enjoy life more.

Spiritual immortality takes a lifetime to achieve.

'Like a butterfly emerging from its cocoon, we ▶
ascend from our physical bodies to start a
new life after death in our spirit bodies'

Breath, Emotions and Two-person Exercises

Breathing techniques

Most people's breathing is controlled by their subconscious mind, and is a reflection of their health. Unhealthy people become breathless after a small amount of exercise. With Tai Chi training, you gain conscious control of your breathing and use it to improve your health.

Special breathing techniques are used which enable greater amounts of the Chi and oxygen from the air to be absorbed into your system. Instead of being breathless, you are Chi-full.

When people breathe normally, it is usually just with their chests. This uses just half of the lung capacity. It is better to use the lungs to full capacity, to increase the oxygenation of the blood and the amount of external Chi taken deeper into the body.

To accomplish this, make your normal breathing long, slow, calm and deep and use Upper Abdominal Breathing (*see page* 47) and at a more advanced level, use Reverse Lower Abdominal Breathing (*see page* 48)

By pumping the body up and increasing the amount of Chi you have inside pushing out, you increase your body's resistance to viruses, bacteria and adverse weather conditions. Strong internal energy strengthens your defensive energy.

Whichever type of breathing you are doing, as you inhale and exhale, the energy moves through the Small Circulation of Chi.

After a few years, once you have consciously programmed these breathing techniques into the subconscious, you will find that they happen by themselves, even when you are not doing Tai Chi.

Your emotions

Breathing techniques can also be used to regulate your mind and emotions: there is a strong connection between the breath, the mind and emotions. For example, when a person gets angry he tends to hold his breath, and when he gets anxious and panics, his breath tends to become shorter and shallower.

In a high pressure situation, you must either intentionally temporarily suppress your emotions and deal with the situation, or, if appropriate, intentionally express your emotions, put your Chi into them, and use them to help you resolve the situation.

In a social situation the expression of emotions is verbal; in a self-defence situation they are released physically through Fa Jing. In training the Fa Jing can be used as an intentional emotional release.

There is no rule about when to suppress or express emotions. The important thing is to be familiar with them, so that they are a help rather than a hindrance when trying to resolve a situation.

So if you can consciously control your breath and get it to work for you, you can regulate your emotions, keep a clear mind and make the right decisions.

Here is a simple example of how to use your breath to help regain your balance when you are angry, anxious or fearful and it is not appropriate for you to express your emotions. Inhale a deep breath through your nose and exhale through your mouth slowly several times. This calms the system and enables you to think more clearly.

There are occasions when it is very beneficial to let your emotions flow. If a person is experiencing grief, expressing it through crying is a release. Staring without blinking is a way to

A Tai Chi posture from the ▶
Old Yang Style of Tai Chi
called 'Immortal points the
way to heaven'

induce crying. If a person experiences great anger, shouting helps to release it.

If it is not appropriate to express the emotion at the time, it is vital to release it later. An emotion rising up to be released is a movement of Chi: if it is suppressed, the Chi flow is blocked, and this can lead to illness developing.

So as well as talking things through to clear the mind, you also have to clear the suppressed emotions from the body. When the trapped emotions have cleared there is easy laughter.

After training Tai Chi and Chi Kung for a few years you find that you can be calm, breathe easily and be focused in circumstances that previously would have made you uncontrollably emotional.

If you bring the emotions under the control of your conscious mind, you can use their energy to help achieve your objectives. For example, when an opponent is about to attack, you experience a combination of fear and anger, both of which release vast amounts of energy into your system. If you know how, you can channel this emotionally generated energy through your Fa Jing. Otherwise, the emotions can be overwhelming and result in you freezing to the spot or succumbing to irrational behaviour.

Two-person training

The two-person training techniques, when done with Fa Jing, enable you to experience something close to the intensity of real combat and to develop reflex actions faster than thought.

Two-person training develops forward pressure and more sensitivity.

Advanced practitioners use considerable forward pressure to develop upper body power and whole body Jing.

There are many two-person training exercises: Pushing Hands and Da Lu are well known examples. In the Old Yang style of Tai Chi there is the San Sau Two-Person Fighting Form, which contains full contact explosive Fa Jing counterstrikes all the way through.

The New Yang Style of Tai Chi has simplified the San Sau, which emphasizes the idea of stepping backwards as the opponent advances, then stepping forwards as he retreats; in the Old Yang Style, when he advances, you also advance with your counterstrike.

All two-person training exercises give you a greater understanding of timing and distance, and increase your sensitivity to other people's energy, which is beneficial for self defence and healing others.

Tao

**The beauty of the Way is
that there is no Way.**
loy ching-yuen

Tao literally means 'The Way'. However, because it is an abstract
idea, each person has their own interpretation of it.

For some people, to follow the Tao means to be in tune with the
natural world. To others, it is about maintaining a healthy balance
in their lives: mentally, emotionally, energetically, physically,
spiritually and socially. Some perceive Tao as their spirit, or the
spirit of the universe. These people aim to follow Tao and be Tao.

Tao cannot be defined simply, because we are all different, and
we must each follow our own path through life, our own Way.

I hope that the information contained in this book will be a small
contribution to your life's journey, and help to bring you a greater
ability in self defence, improve your health and wellbeing and
enhance your self and spiritual development.

Resources

There are many good teachers who are not part of any school or association. To find out where Tai Chi is taught, look in the alternative health advertising sections of local papers or listings magazines, and at the back of martial arts magazines. Many sports centres and health clubs offer Tai Chi classes, so ring them to see what is available. If there are a few places to learn Tai Chi nearby, watch or join in a class at each place before you choose.

The World Taiji Boxing Association

The World Taiji Boxing Association has its headquarters in Australia and members in 35 different countries. As well as having qualified instructors it has an information centre called MTG Publishing which produces over 200 videos on all aspects of the internal martial arts and a quarterly magazine called *Combat and Healing*.

WTBA instructors in the United Kingdom

For an up-to-date list of Tai Chi instructors in the UK call Paul Brecher. He is the senior London representative of the WTBA and can be contacted on 020 8264 8074 or at www.taiji.net or paul@taiji.net.

Information on WTBA instructors overseas

Contact Master Erle Montaigue, PO Box 792, Murwillumbah, NSW 2484, Australia www.taijiworld.com.

About the Author

At a high level of skill the practitioner has pride over his ability, rejoices in praise from others, and laments the lack of ability in others. At the highest level, a man has the look of knowing nothing.
ancient Taoist wisdom

Paul Brecher has over 20 years of experience in the martial arts and is a senior instructor of the World Taiji Boxing Association. He has written numerous articles for magazines and given Tai Chi demonstrations on television.

In his London classes he teaches Yang Lu Chan's Old Yang Style Tai Chi Long Form, the large and small Old Yang Style Tai Chi San Sau Two-Person Fighting Form, the Old Yang Style Pauchui Cannon Fist Form, and Tai Chi Weapons Forms. He also teaches Pushing Hands, Da Lu, Tai Chi Lung Har Chuan (Dragon Prawn Boxing), Three Circle Chi Kung, the Small Circulation and Large Circulation of Chi, Iron Shirt and Iron Palm Chi Kung and the Twelve Circular Tai Chi Dim Mak Palms.

As well as being involved with the martial arts, he is a practitioner of Traditional Chinese Medicine.

Paul Brecher BA MAcS MPCHM (Bachelor of Arts, Member of the Acupuncture Society, and Member Practitioner of Chinese Herbal Medicine) can be contacted at the following address:

PO BOX 13219, London NW11 7WS. Tel: 020 8264 8074, paul@taiji.net or www.taiji.net.